REAL-TIME feedb

IT'S ALWAYS A GOOD TIME TO GIVE FEEDBACK.

Use this real-time feedback tool to practise writing feedback for your colleagues.

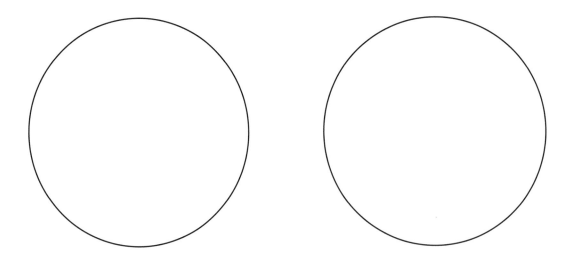

REINVENT THE WHEEL

SEE HOW MANY NEW AND INTERESTING WAYS YOU CAN
DRAW A WHEEL. THIS WILL PREPARE YOU FOR THAT DAY-
LONG BRAINSTORMING MEETING COMING UP.

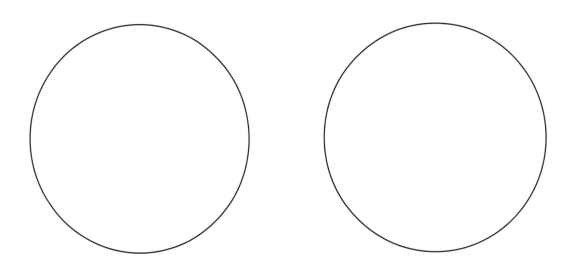

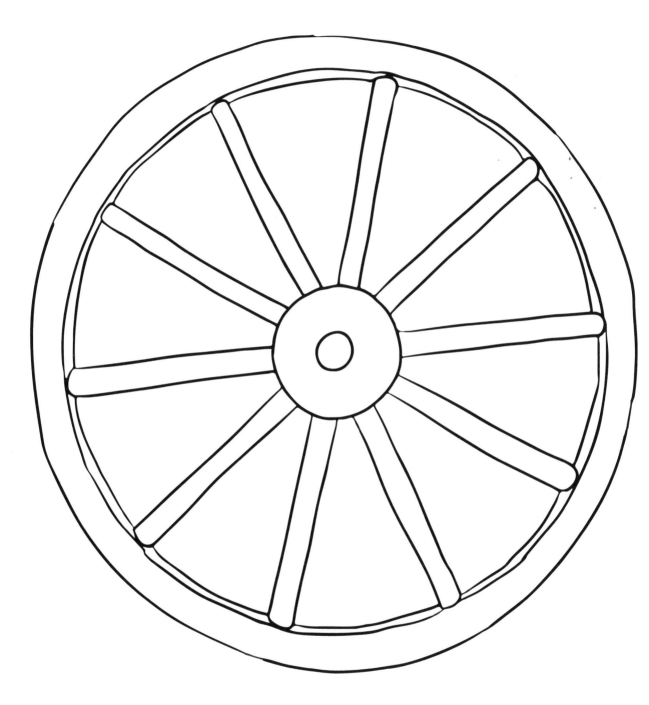

DRAW WHAT SUCCESS LOOKS LIKE

THE COLOURING AND ACTIVITY BOOK FOR SERIOUS BUSINESSPEOPLE

SARAH COOPER ☺ THECOOPERREVIEW.COM

◩ SQUARE PEG

HOW DOES THIS
FIT INTO
THE BIG PICTURE?

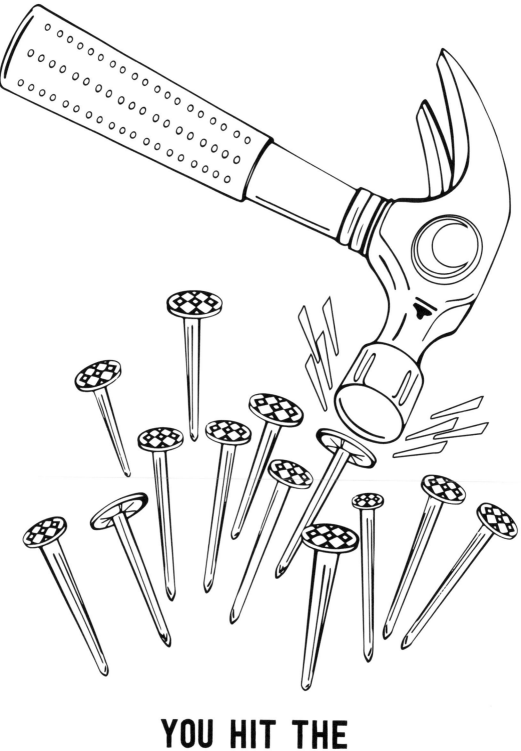

YOU HIT THE

NAIL ON THE HEAD

KEY METRICS TRACKER

KEEP TRACK OF WHENEVER ANYONE SAYS IT, INCLUDING YOURSELF.

CAN WE TAKE A STEP BACK HERE? _____

WHAT PROBLEM ARE WE TRYING TO SOLVE? _____

I SEE YOUR CONCERN _____

LET'S GET THE BALL ROLLING _____

LET'S TABLE THAT FOR NOW _____

CAN I JUMP IN HERE? _____

INTERESTING POINT _____

DO WE HAVE ANY DATA? _____

WILL THIS SCALE? _____

WHAT ARE THE TAKEAWAYS? _____

WHO CAN TAKE THIS ACTION ITEM? _____

WHAT ARE THE NEXT STEPS? _____

LET'S SCHEDULE A MEETING TO DISCUSS THAT _____

WHAT ARE THE BEST PRACTICES? _____

LET'S FOLLOW UP _____

FIND
THE UNICORN

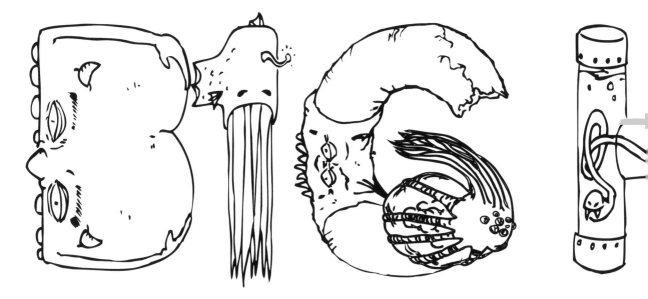

TRY TO MAKE THIS B.H.A.G.

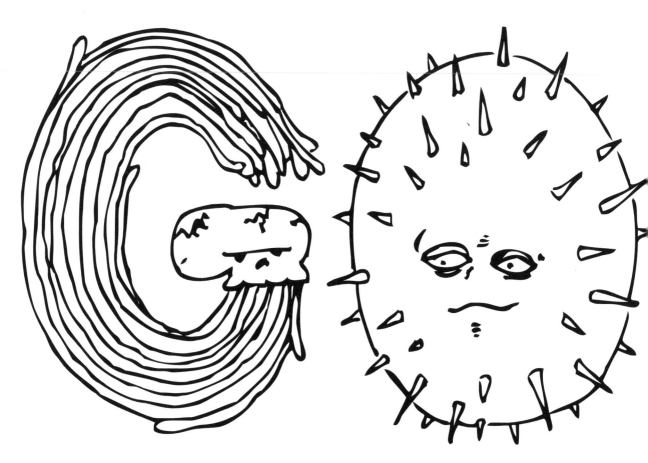

BIGGER & HAIRIER & SCARIER

RESIGNATION E-MAIL AD LIBS

Fellow _____,

_____fun name for your team_

It's with _____ that I must share with you my

_____something sad, e.g., 'a heavy heart'_

decision to leave _____. This was a very difficult

_____name of company_

decision to make.

It's hard to believe that _____ ago, I was the _____.

_____how long you've been there_____your first position_

From that time until when I was _____, and all the way

_____your second position_

to my current role as _____, I have grown so much. I've

_____current position_

learned so much, and hopefully taught all of you in return.

I am heading off to explore my next chapter _____

_____.

_____the much more awesome thing you'll be doing_

I'm excited about my future while I continue to be excited about

all the things you'll continue to accomplish here (except for you,

_____, you never finish anything)!

person everyone

always makes fun of

If I could leave you all with just one thought, please remember

these words: _____.

_____sage advice or Steve Jobs' quote you found on Google_

If you ever want to get in touch, my info is below.

This isn't goodbye; our paths will cross again. Hopefully at my

leaving drinks at _____!
　　　　　　　　　　　　date and time

_____
　　　　　　your name

_____
　　　　　phone number

_____
　　　　e-mail address

_____
　　　　　　blog

_____
　　　　　LinkedIn

_____
　　　　　Twitter

_____
　　　　　Facebook

_____
　　　　　Snapchat

_____
social media platform no one's ever heard of

WHAT'S ON YOUR RADAR?

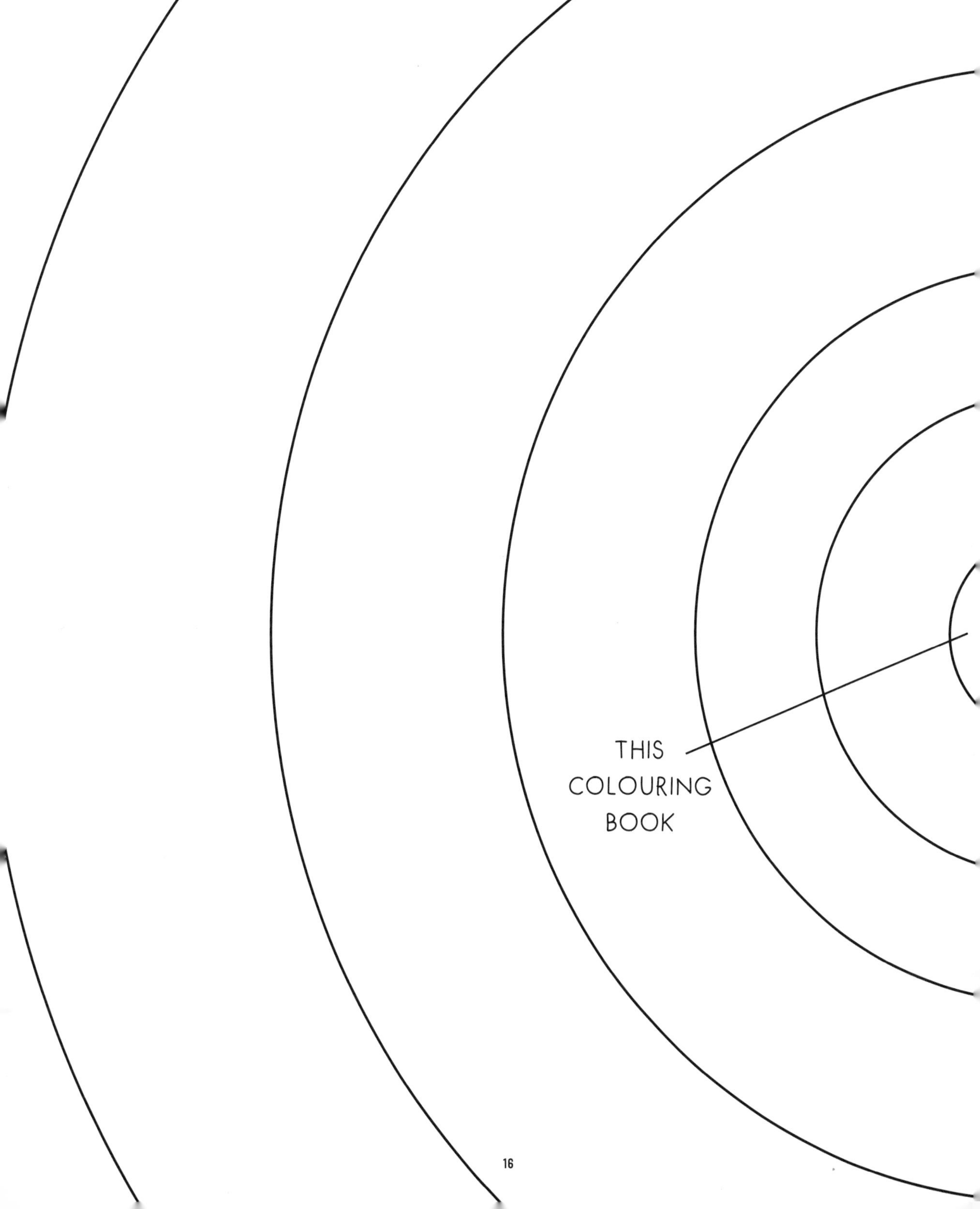

THIS
COLOURING
BOOK

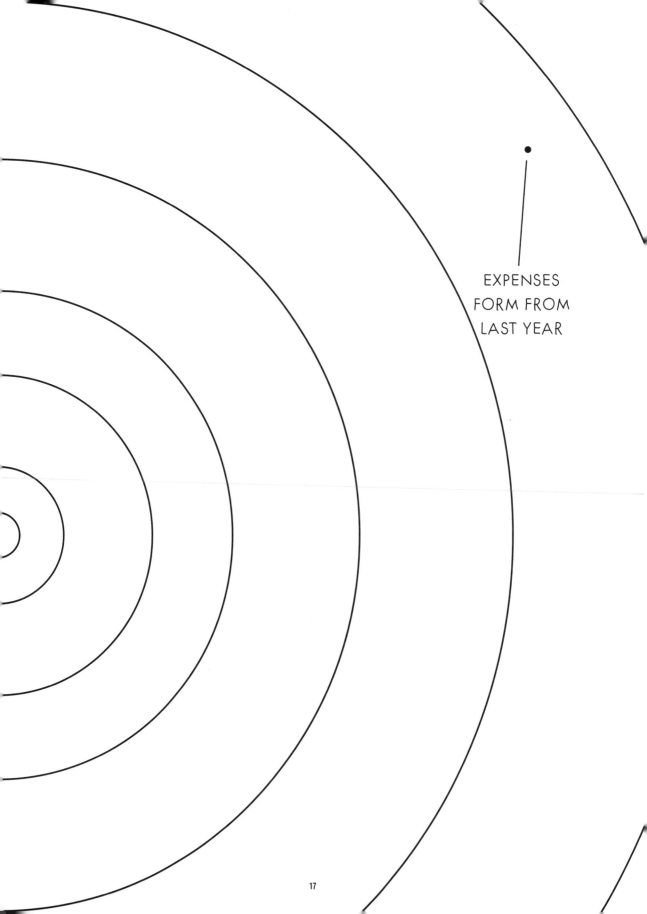

EXPENSES
FORM FROM
LAST YEAR

NAME THE MOVIE

THESE FUN PHRASES CAME STRAIGHT FROM HOLLYWOOD
(WHO TOOK THEM STRAIGHT FROM SERIOUS BUSINESSPEOPLE).

'I DRINK YOUR MILKSHAKE' _____

'I COULD TELL YOU, BUT THEN I'D HAVE TO KILL YOU' _____

'ALWAYS BE CLOSING' _____

'DANGER IS MY MIDDLE NAME' _____

'WE'RE NOT IN KANSAS ANYMORE' _____

'I'M GONNA MAKE HIM AN OFFER HE CAN'T REFUSE' _____

'WHAT WE'VE GOT HERE IS FAILURE TO COMMUNICATE' _____

'YOU CAN'T HANDLE THE TRUTH' _____

'SHOW ME THE MONEY' _____

'ROUND UP THE USUAL SUSPECTS' _____

'I'LL BE BACK' _____

'HOUSTON, WE HAVE A PROBLEM' _____

'I'M THE KING OF THE WORLD!' _____

'KEEP YOUR FRIENDS CLOSE BUT YOUR ENEMIES CLOSER' _____

ANSWER KEY: Look it up on Google.

ARE YOU READY FOR
THE BIG PITCH?

KNOCK IT OUT
OF THE PARK!

EMERGENCY DISGUISE

EVERYONE'S DOING A GREAT JOB

EXCEPT FOR:

_____

FLIP-FLOPPING

COLOUR IN THE FLIP-FLOPS FOR A LITTLE THERAPEUTIC
RELEASE FROM INDECISIVE LEADERS.

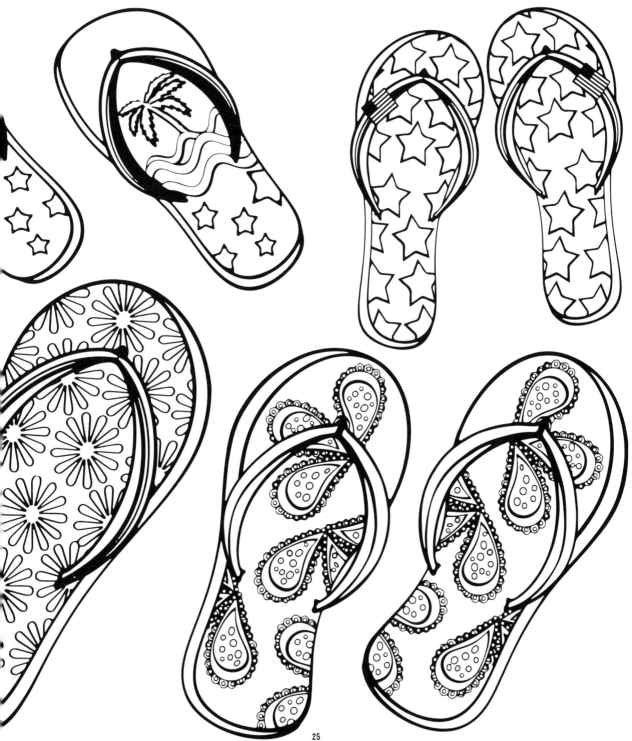

PEER REVIEW WORKSHEET

USE THIS WORKSHEET TO CONSTRUCT AS MANY SENTENCES AS
YOU NEED FOR YOUR PEER REVIEW MINIMUM WORD COUNT.

deep	passion	priorities
mediocre	grasp	consensus
arbitrary	handle	strategy
excellent	focus	how to execute
surprising	understanding	key insights
unnecessary	knowledge	big data
credible	mastery	useless details
pragmatic	acuity	team building
disappointing	perspicacity	mentoring
painful	ownership	deliverables
weird	approach	iteration
triumphant	orientation	design aesthetic
inspiring	cultivation	relationships
nebulous	expertise	vision

EXAMPLE:

Ben has a mediocre grasp of strategy. He has a
disappointing understanding of useless details.
Ben also has a painful focus on how to execute.

GET OUT OF YOUR COMFORT ZONE

COMFORT ZONE
↓

↓
PROMOTION

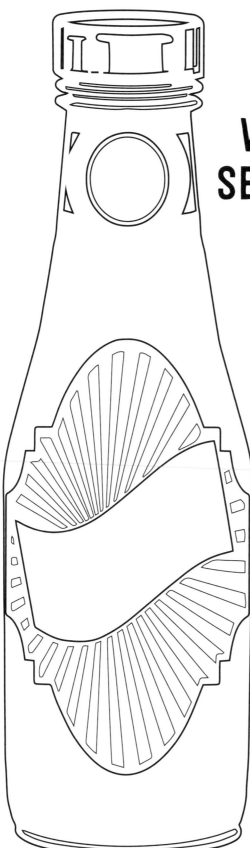

WHAT'S YOUR SECRET SAUCE?

Design your secret sauce bottle and list the ingredients (but don't let your competitors see!).

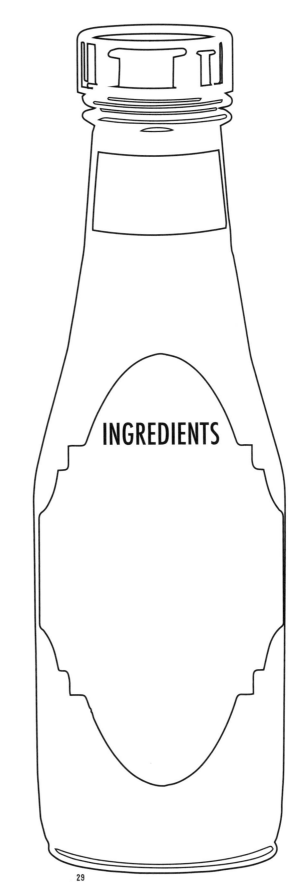

INGREDIENTS

It's OK to recycle your ingredients from other, more successful products.

WHAT ARE THE TAKEAWAYS?

Pretend to write down the key takeaways here.

_____

_____

_____

_____

_____

_____

_____

_____

_____

_____

_____

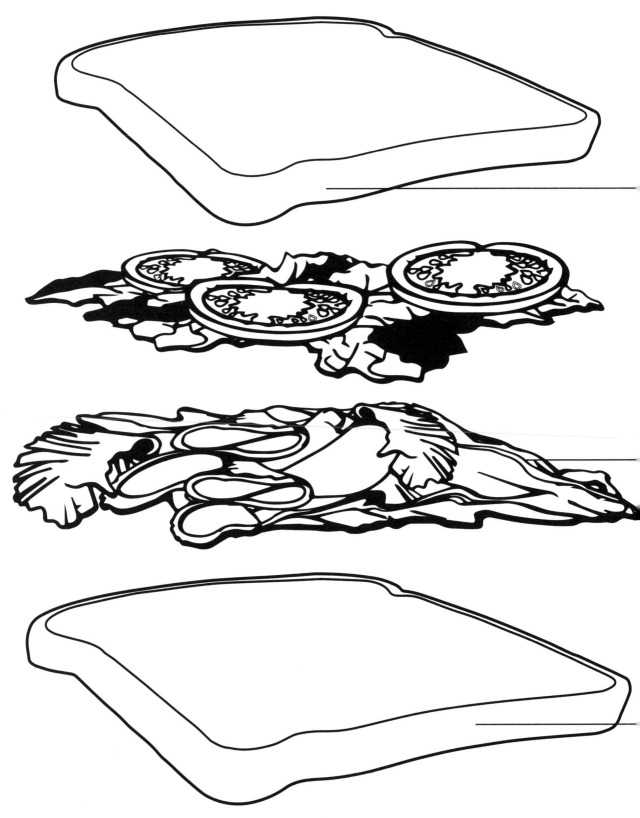

PRAISE-SANDWICH WORKSHEET

Practise sandwiching your criticism between
two thin slices of compliments.

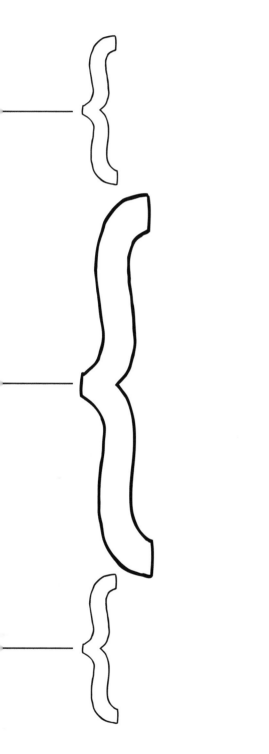

COMPLIMENTS

CRITICISM

COMPLIMENTS

WHAT COLOUR
ARE YOUR
HANDCUFFS?

YOUR STOCKS ARE VESTING!

Celebrate by colouring in these decorative vests.

CRUNCH THE NUMBERS

ANALYSE THE DATA

Plot the points to see how your product did this quarter.

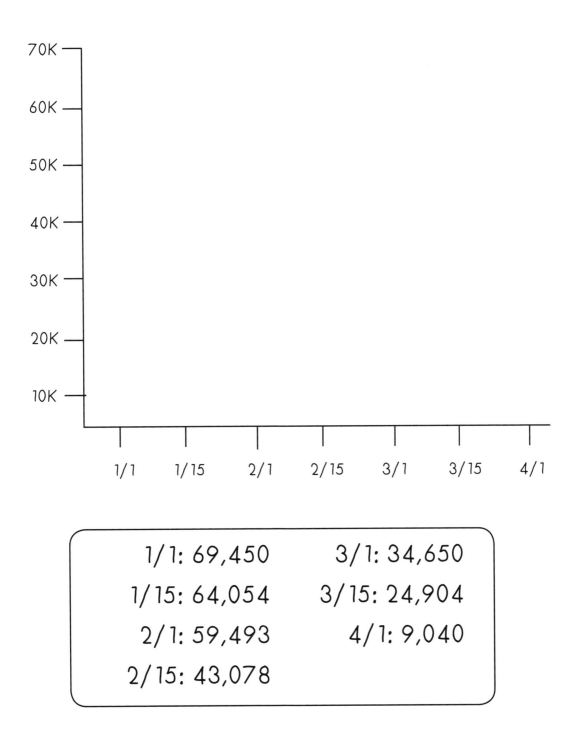

1/1: 69,450	3/1: 34,650
1/15: 64,054	3/15: 24,904
2/1: 59,493	4/1: 9,040
2/15: 43,078	

GOOD IDEA GRAVEYARD

RIP

Here lies
my idea for
Massage
Mondays.
Born: Dec. 3
Died: Dec. 3

WRITE DOWN ALL THE GREAT IDEAS YOU'VE HAD OVER
THE YEARS THAT WILL NEVER SEE THE LIGHT OF DAY.

DO YOU HAVE
A BUSINESS MODEL?

Make your business model
as attractive as possible
before you meet with
potential investors.

MEETING OFFENDERS

THE ONE WHO'S NOT REALLY THERE

This person uses the meeting to catch up on e-mail (or sleep)

THE HUMBLEBRAGGER

Always says things like, 'I was just chatting with the CEO'

THE OVERPROMISER

Will say, 'We can get that done by tomorrow, right?'

THE BULLDOZER

Always quick to interrupt if he doesn't like what he's hearing

EACH OFFICE HAS THEM. DRAW THE PROFILE OF
THE PERSON WHO BEST FITS THE PROFILE.

THE WHISPERER

Always in sidebar
conversations, and when
asked to speak up, says,
'Oh, nothing'

THE DUCKER

Will schedule a meeting,
show up, then leave
when he feels like it

THE TAPPER

Taps his feet, his
fingers, his pencil,
and/or sighs loudly

THE OVERTHANKER

Always thanking
everyone for everything

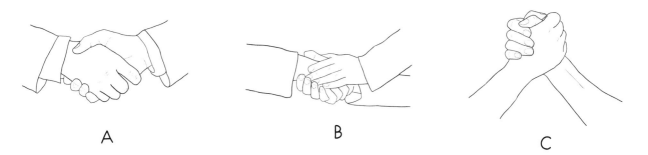

A

B

C

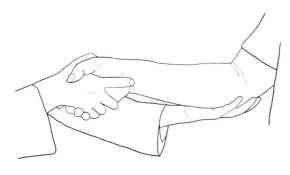

D

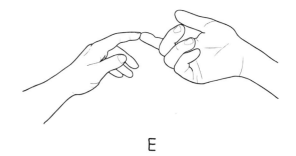

E

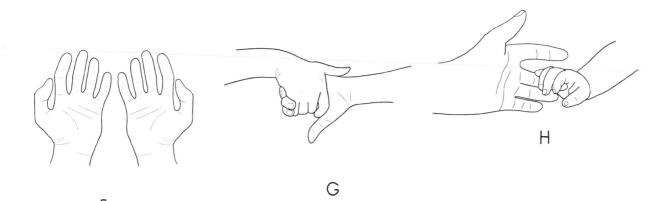

F

G

H

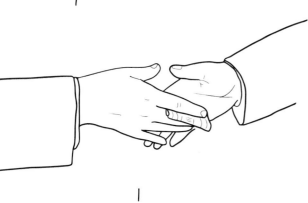

I

J

44

HANDSHAKE QUIZ

NAME A FEW SITUATIONS WHERE THIS GREETING MIGHT BE APPROPRIATE.

A networking event, client meeting,

B job interview,

C poker night,

D volunteering,

E drunken leaving party,

F McDonalds,

G awkward good-bye,

H boss's baby shower,

I street corner,

J team building event,

IS IT REPEATABLE?

Draw this exact same shape as many times as you can.

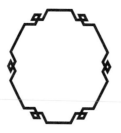

WILL IT SCALE?

Draw bigger and bigger triangles to see if it will scale.

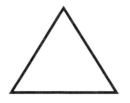

EMOTIONAL INTELLIGENCE QUIZ

_____   _____   _____

WHAT IS THE FACE SAYING?

WRITE DOWN THE EMOTION TO MATCH THE FACE.

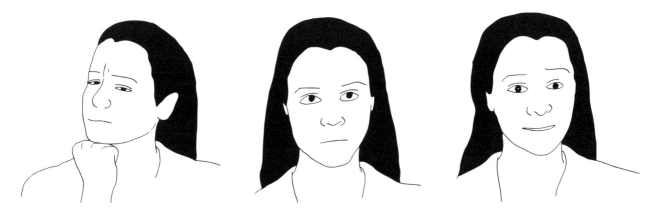

_____   _____   _____

'GREAT SPEECH, BOSS.'

'OH, RIGHT! WE DID FORGET
TO DOCUMENT THAT
DECISION.'

'IS ANYONE WRITING
THIS DOWN?'

HOW DO YOU MAKE THAT FACE?

DRAW THE FACE TO MATCH THE EMOTION.

'HEY! IT'S ALMOST BEER:30!'

'WHO KEEPS SCHEDULING
MEETINGS FOR 8 AM?'

'SORRY,
MOUTH FULL.'

WHAT DOES SUCCESS LOOK LIKE?

DRAW SUCCESS HERE.

WHAT DOES FAILURE LOOK LIKE?

DRAW FAILURE HERE.

MEETING SPEAK

MATCH THE COMMON MEETING PHRASE
TO WHAT IT REALLY MEANS.

This wasn't in my diary	I'm pretty sure you're wrong
Duly noted	I need this to be over
Let's table that	I'll do the bare minimum
Can you repeat that?	Probably not
To your earlier point...	Let's keep talking about this forever
That said...	I have no idea what you're saying
It's a no-brainer	You will never hear from me again
Definitely	We are going to be here a while
Can I ask a quick question?	Don't ever bring this up again
Happy to discuss this further	I'd like to change the subject
Let's streamline this process	I deleted this from my diary
Sounds good to me	I've already forgotten about it
Let's get some data on that	I was looking at Facebook
I'll try my best	We're still not changing anything
Let's circle back later	I don't feel like thinking about it
I'll set a reminder to follow up	I'm kissing your ass
On a related note...	That's the dumbest thing I've ever heard

WOULD YOU RATHER?

CIRCLE THE THING YOU'D RATHER DO THAN ATTEND THIS MEETING.

Walk on hot coals	Attend this meeting
Walk on glass	Attend this meeting
Walk 500 miles	Attend this meeting
Eat an ant	Attend this meeting
Skydive	Attend this meeting
Skydive without training	Attend this meeting
Skydive without a parachute	Attend this meeting
Have root canal	Attend this meeting
Perform root canal	Attend this meeting
Go to a Nickelback concert	Attend this meeting
Enter a clog-dancing contest	Attend this meeting
Drink unpasteurised milk	Attend this meeting
Be on a reality TV show	Attend this meeting
Win then lose 1 billion pounds	Attend this meeting
Testify before the High Court	Attend this meeting
Live in a cave	Attend this meeting

ARE YOU ADDING VALUE?

Add these values to show how much value you can add.

610 + 37	412 + 73	417 + 2	415 + 80	440 + 59
244 + 34	644 x 2	363 + 36	720 + 74	736 + 10
263 + 14	322 + 75	730 + 21	562 + 72	241 + 41
141 + 25	142 + 41	328 + 28	342 + 17	640 + 13
362 + 21	520 + 29	571 + 23	226 + 10	216 + 64

PRETEND TO TAKE NOTES

Write down every other word you hear, while nodding.
Circle or double-underline every so often.

_____

_____

_____

_____

_____

_____

_____

_____

_____

_____

_____

WE NEED TO
DRILL DOWN

DIVERSITY INITIATIVE

Our team isn't diverse enough! Use your drawing and
colouring skills to create a truly diverse team.

THINK BIG

DRAW THE BIGGEST THINGS YOU CAN THINK OF.

BLUE SKY

Put your deepest thoughts into the clouds.

MANIFESTO AD LIBS

_____ ago, I enthusiastically joined _____. It has
how long ago you joined   *name of company*

been a _____ experience. I proudly bleed _____
          positive adjective   *company colours*

every day! I even have a temporary tattoo of the _____
                                                  name of company logo

on the back of my leg.

But all is not _____. _____ recently wrote an
                positive noun   *news publication*

article about us, detailing our terrible record on _____.
                                                    what your company has
                                                    a terrible record on

I wanted to share what I think is _____ and recommend a
                                  negative adjective

path forward.

Our Three Problems

1. We lack a focussed, cohesive _____.
                                 the thing your company lacks

We've known this for _____, but have done nothing about it. I've
                     vague amount of time

heard our _____ described as _____.
          noun   *food metaphor for bad strategy*

I hate _____. We all should.
       food from previous metaphor

2. We don't have clear _____.
                        thing that's not clear

The most painful manifestation of this is the massive _____
                                                      big problem with
                                                      your company

that exists throughout the organisation. There's a reason

why _____. We're not doing that.
    sport metaphor about
    how to win a game

3. We lack _____.

the other thing your company lacks

Combine _____ with _____, and the result is

first problem   *second problem*

_____.

third problem

Solving Our Problems

1. Focus on _____.

what your company should focus on

We need to get rid of _____ and eliminate _____.

first thing to get rid of   *second thing to get rid of*

2. Restore _____.

what your company should restore

By building around a strong _____ structure, we will

jargon

eliminate significant _____.

what you'll eliminate

3. Blow up the _____ and kill the _____.

what needs to be blown up (figuratively)   *what needs to be killed (figuratively)*

Empower a new model of _____. Align a set

some model you read in a business book

of _____ so that they are not _____.

important sounding nouns   *the thing they shouldn't be doing*

This won't be easy. It will take _____. I very much

positive nouns, e.g., 'tenacity'

look forward to the challenge. Let's _____ and stop

thing to do from the earlier sport metaphor

eating _____.

the bad thing from the earlier food metaphor

HOW SOON UNTIL YOU BURN OUT?

I was last on the
To: line in an
e-mail from my
boss to the team

WHEN SOMETHING STRESSFUL HAPPENS, ADD IT HERE.
THEN YOU CAN COUNT DOWN THE DAYS UNTIL
YOU REACH THE END OF YOUR ROPE.

INTERVIEW QUESTIONS TRACKER

Keep track of whenever you ask it.

WHY DO YOU WANT TO WORK HERE? _____

WHAT ARE YOUR STRENGTHS? _____

WHAT ARE YOUR WEAKNESSES? _____

HOW WOULD YOU DIG
YOUR WAY OUT OF A HOLE? _____

IF YOU WERE ME, WOULD YOU HIRE YOU? _____

IF I WERE YOU, WOULD YOU
WANT ME TO HIRE ME? _____

HOW OLD ARE YOU? UH, I MEAN,
WHAT YEAR DID YOU GRADUATE? _____

WHAT DO YOU LIKE TO DO FOR FUN? _____

WHAT IS THE BIGGEST CHALLENGE
YOU'VE EVER FACED? _____

TELL ME ABOUT A TIME WHEN YOU LOST
YOUR KEYS. HOW DID YOU FIND THEM? _____

CAN YOU HELP ME FIX MY WEBSITE? _____

HOW DO YOU FEEL ABOUT TABLE TENNIS? _____

MAKE AN IMPACT

HIT THIS PAGE AS HARD AS YOU CAN

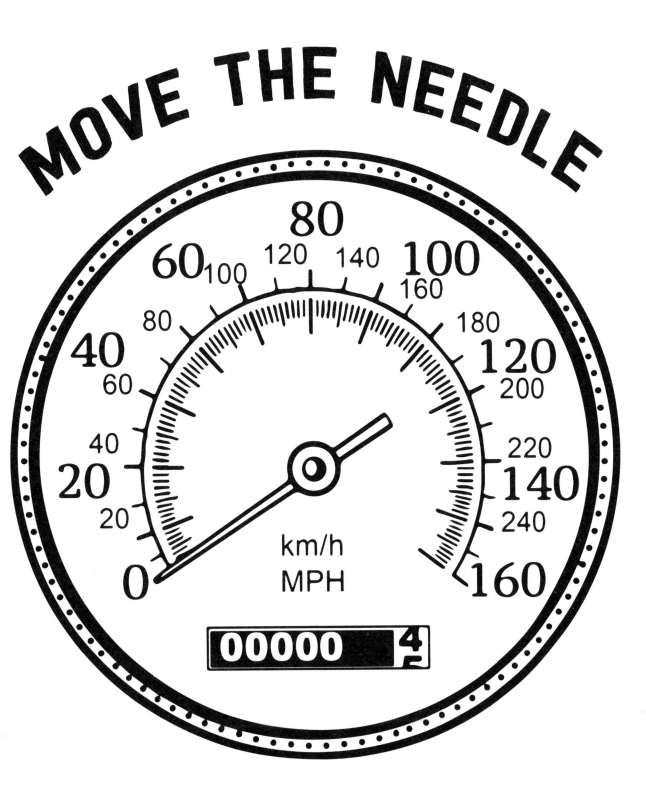

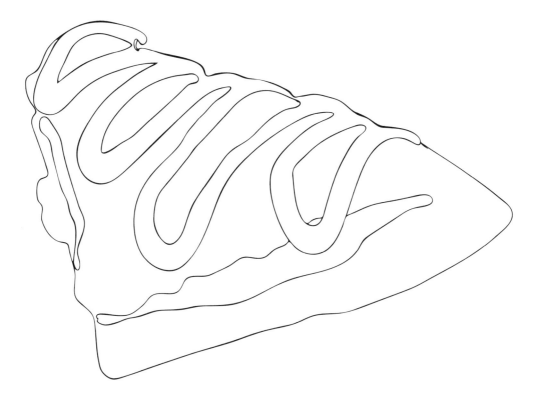

REDUCE TURNOVER

Draw a smaller version of this delicious apple turnover.

COLLEAGUE CARD WORKSHEET

Happy
Birthday!

Feel
Better!

Practise what you're going to write in your colleague's card before you go screwing it up in the real thing.

Welcome Back!

Sorry to See You Go!

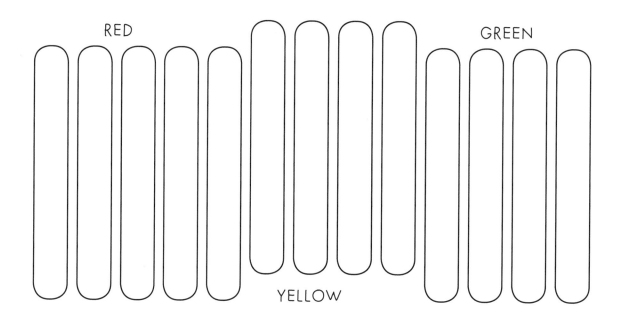

RED

GREEN

YELLOW

CHANGE YOUR TONE

SOMEONE DOESN'T LIKE YOUR TONE?
PRACTICE CHANGING YOUR TONE BY COLOURING
DIFFERENT SHADES HERE.

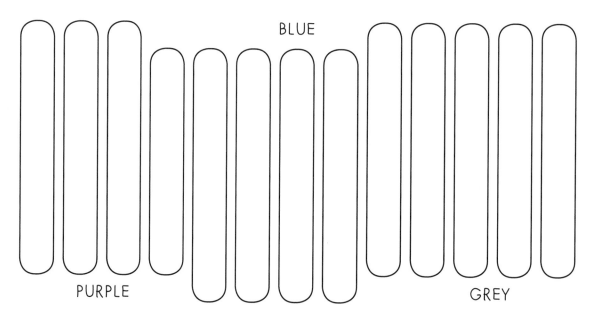

BLUE

PURPLE

GREY

GET ON THE SAME PAGE

Get all of your colleagues to look at this page at the same time.
This will be a huge accomplishment.

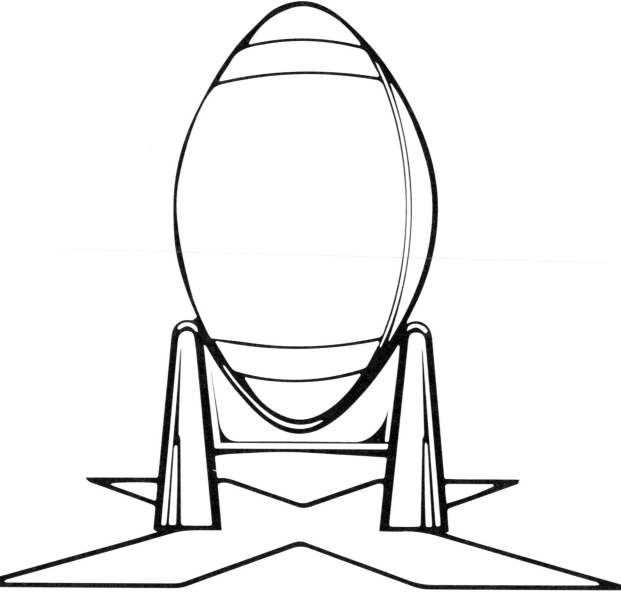

MEETING HALL OF FAME

Keep track of all the types of meetings you've been to.
You get a prize for each one. But not really.

KICK-OFF MEETING   _____

FOLLOW-UP MEETING   _____

TEAM UPDATE   _____

BRAINSTORMING MEETING   _____

1-ON-1 WITH MY MANAGER   _____

1-ON-1 WITH MY DIRECT REPORT   _____

1-ON-1 WITH MY INTERN   _____

SKIP LEVEL 1-ON-1   _____

PAINFUL NETWORKING EVENT   _____

3-HOUR CONFERENCE CALL   _____

VIDEO CONFERENCE CALL   _____

NO IDEA WHY WE'RE MEETING   _____

EXIT INTERVIEW AFTER BEING FIRED   _____

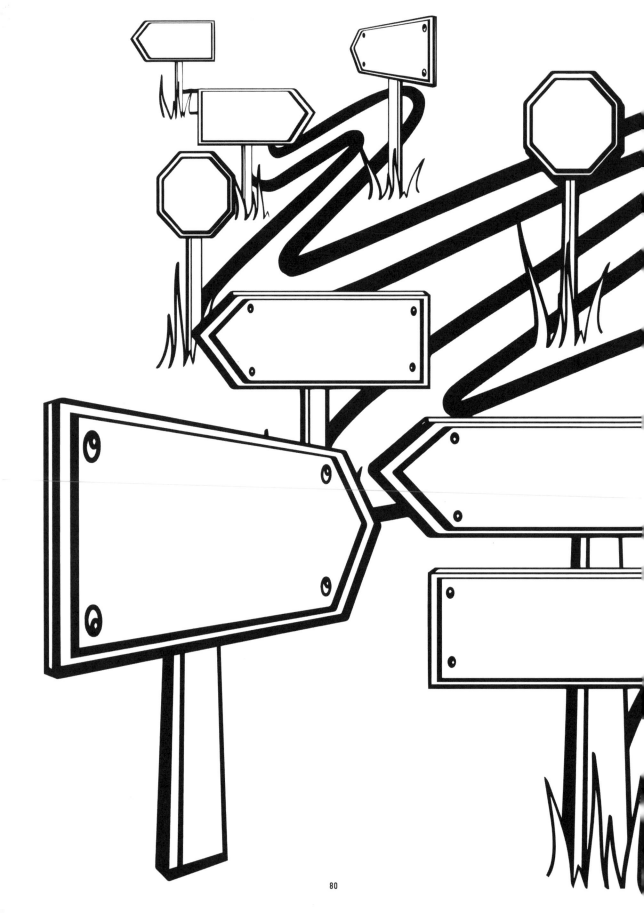

WHAT IS THE
ROADMAP?

Put all your important
milestones in the signs.

M1

BUILD YOUR
STRAW MAN

BEST OF BREED

Draw your best-of-breed solutions.

GET ALL
YOUR DUCKS
IN A ROW

WHAT'S ON YOUR PLATE?

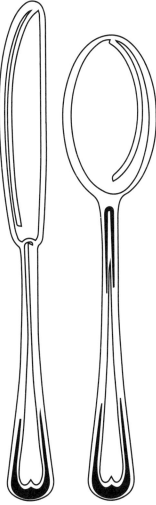

EXIT STRATEGY

You have multiple exits! Pick your favourite one and colour it.

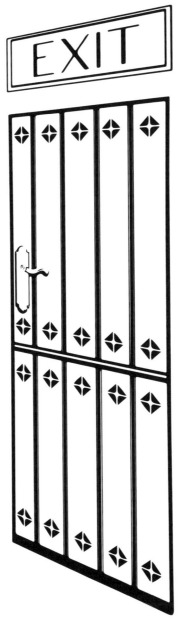

COMPANY CULTURE

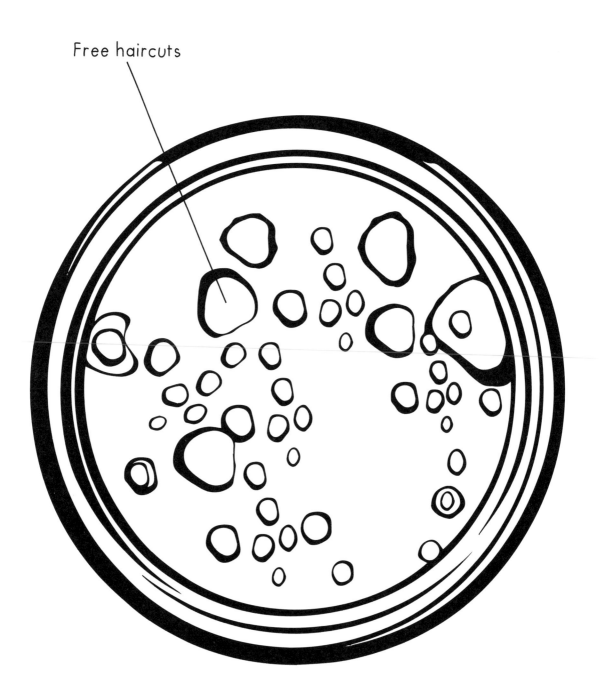

Free haircuts

YOUR COMPANY'S CULTURE IS VERY IMPORTANT.
CREATE A CULTURE YOU'D BE PROUD OF AND
NEVER EVER WANT TO LEAVE.

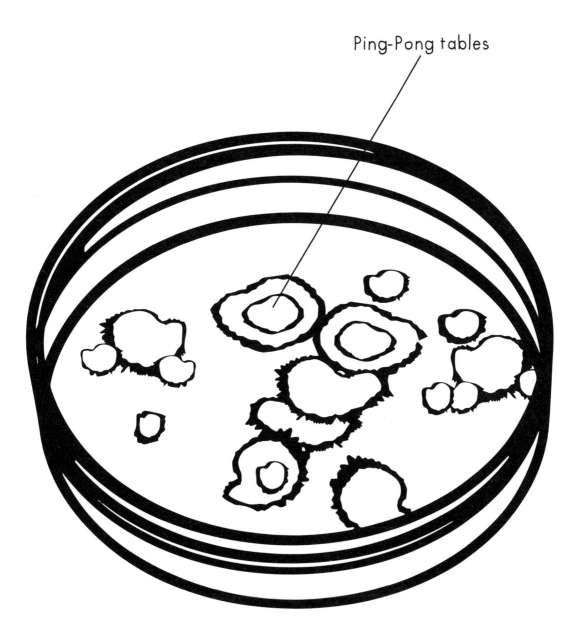

Ping-Pong tables

ESCALATOR

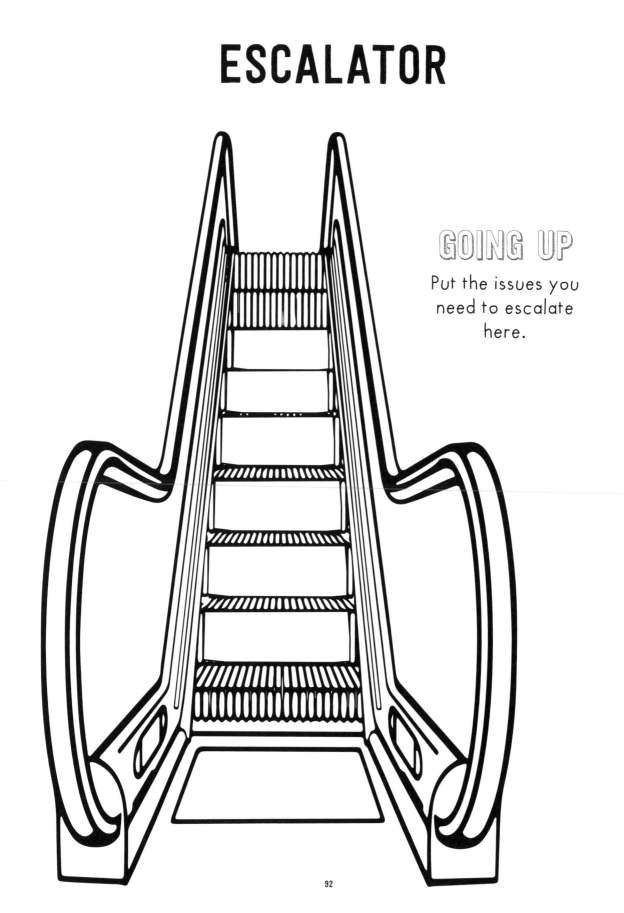

GOING UP

Put the issues you
need to escalate
here.

DE-ESCALATOR

GOING DOWN

Put the issues you
need to de-escalate
here.

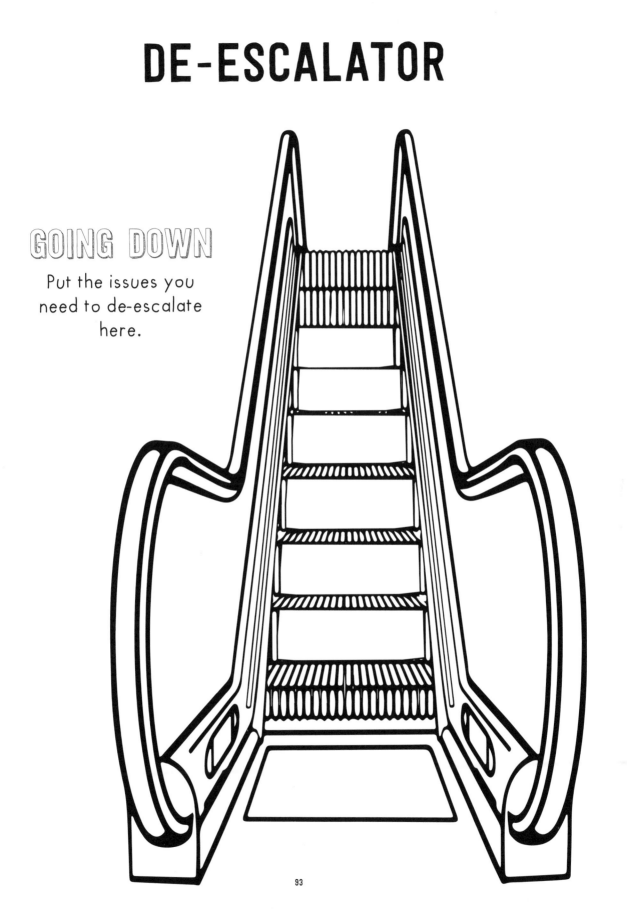

WHAT DO YOU BRING
TO THE TABLE?

Draw everything you bring to the table so that a potential employer can see all the reasons to employ you.

FOCUS ON
EXECUTING
BLEEDING-EDGE
TECHNOLOGY

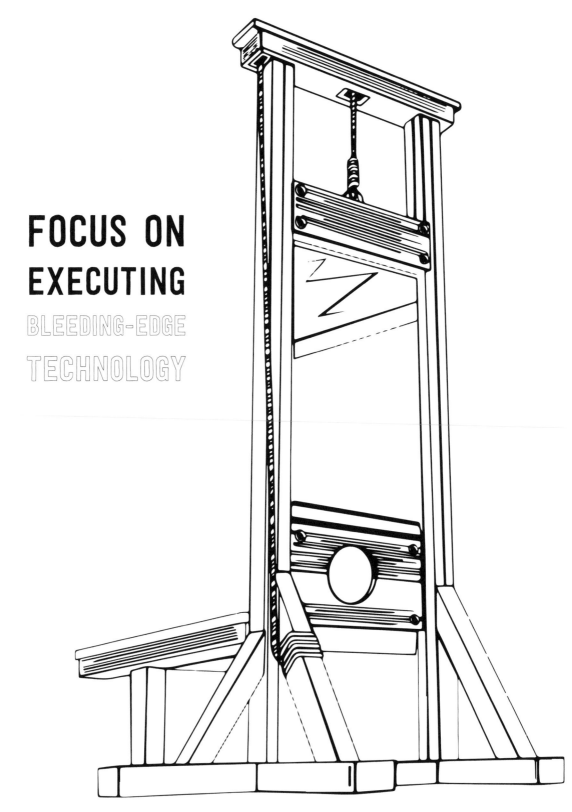

I DON'T SEE ANY
RED FLAGS.

DRAW SOME RED FLAGS HERE.

ARE YOU LASER-FOCUSSED?

OUTLINE AND COLOUR THE LASERS
SO THEY'RE MORE FOCUSSED, LIKE YOU ARE.

FIRE ON ALL CYLINDERS

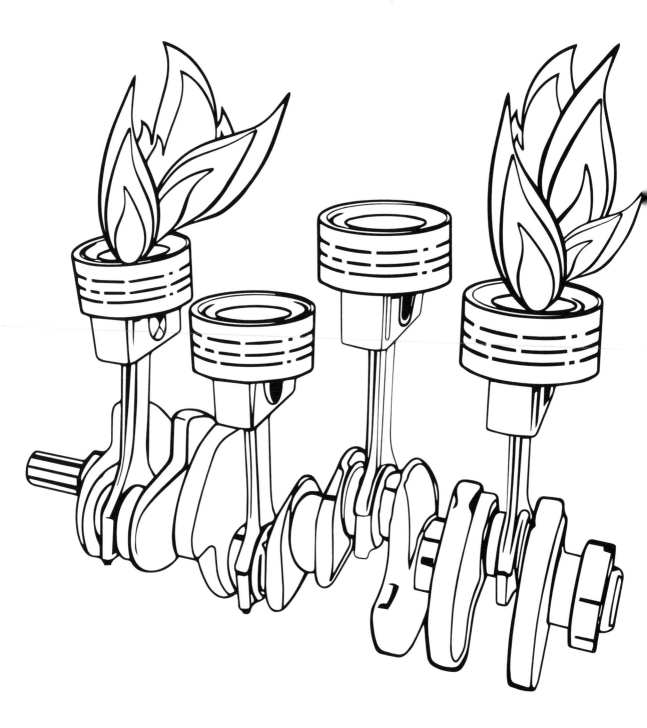

Not all cylinders are firing! Draw a fire in all cylinders.

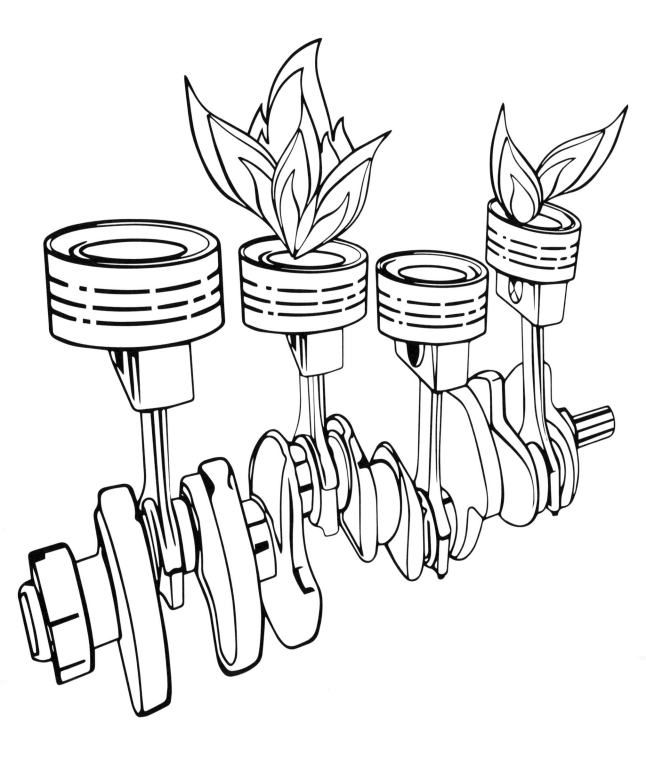

UNCANNY VALLEY

UH-OH. WE'VE REACHED AN UNCANNY VALLEY.
MAKE THE VALLEYS MORE SIMILAR, OR MORE DIFFERENT.

LET'S
JOIN
THE DOTS

DEVIL'S ADVOCATE PRACTISE

Write down the opposite of each statement to
practise playing devil's advocate.

WE DON'T NEED DATA   But what if..._____

IT'S GOOD ENOUGH   But what if..._____

WE CAN DO IT LATER   But what if..._____

THIS IS A GREAT IDEA   But what if..._____

LET'S SHARE THIS
WITH THE TEAM   But what if..._____

OUR CUSTOMERS WON'T
NOTICE THAT   But what if..._____

YOU CAN HANDLE THIS
ON YOUR OWN   But what if..._____

OUR CLIENTS NEED THIS   But what if..._____

THIS PROJECT WAS SUCCESSFUL   But what if..._____

WE CAN DO IT BETTER   But what if..._____

LET'S COME UP WITH
A NEW STRATEGY   But what if..._____

LET'S FIX THE
UNDERLYING PROBLEM   But what if..._____

WORK-LIFE BALANCE

Your work-life balance is all out of whack.
Add a few things to the life side
to even it out again.

WHAT IS OUR BENCH- MARK?

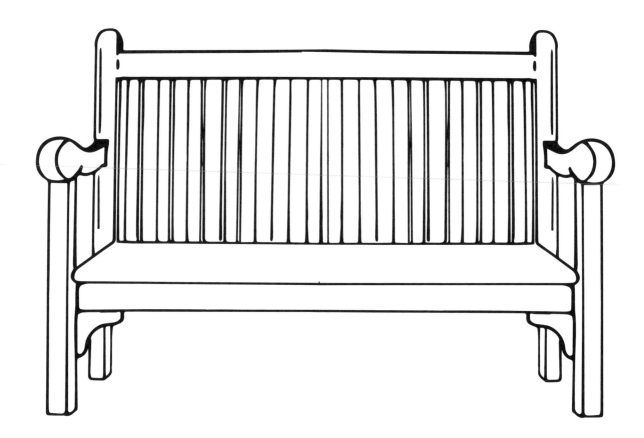

DRAW A MARK SITTING ON THIS BENCH.

WHO'S DRIVING THIS?

Right now, no one is.
Draw someone driving this before the whole project crashes.

LOW-
HANGING
FRUIT

ACTION FIGURES

TIME
TO
PIVOT

POSTMORTEM AD LIBS

Team,

This has been an incredible _____. We've had some high points,
                              time period

such as _____, and some low points, such as _____.
         thing that went well   thing that didn't go well

I want to talk to you more about _____ to see where we went
                                  thing that didn't go well

wrong and what we can do better next time.

First, the team we assembled was _____, but there was
                                  positive adjective

no clear _____. This should have been fixed immediately.
          something that was missing

_____ and I have taken responsibility for that, but obviously
 employee name

the responsibility lies with all of us.

Second, our _____ started out strong but then became
             noun, pural

really _____. What went wrong there? I am _____
        negative adjective   adjective

to hear your thoughts.

Finally, right in the middle of the project, _____. This was
                                              unexpected thing that happened

completely unavoidable by all accounts.

Thank you, everyone, for your _____ work on this. I know
                               positive adjective

it will go better next time.

WHAT ARE YOUR NEXT STEPS?

1 3 5 7 9 10 8 6 4 2

Square Peg, an imprint of Vintage,

20 Vauxhall Bridge Road,

London SW1V 2SA

Square Peg is part of the Penguin Random House group of companies
whose addresses can be found at global.penguinrandomhouse.com.

Penguin
Random House
UK

First published by Square Peg in 2016

www.vintage-books.co.uk

A CIP catalogue record for this book is available from the British Library

ISBN 9781910931172

Additional illustrations by Dawn Larder
Designer, Art Director: Diane Marsh

Printed in Italy by L.E.G.O. S.p.A.

Penguin Random House is committed to a sustainable future for our business, our readers
and our planet. This book is made from Forest Stewardship Council® certified paper.